Edexcel
GCSE MODULAR MATHEMATICS
Homework and Consolidation

INTERMEDIATE

Stage 1

**Karen Hughes   Trevor Johnson   Peter Jolly
David Kent   Keith Pledger**

Heinemann

Edexcel
Success through qualifications

Heinemann Educational Publishers,
Halley Court, Jordan Hill, Oxford, OX2 8EJ
Part of Harcourt Education

© Karen Hughes, Trevor Johnson, Peter Jolly, David Kent, Keith Pledger, 2003

First published 2003

08 07 06 05 04 03
10 9 8 7 6 5 4 3 2 1

British Library Cataloguing in Publication Data is available from the British Library on request.

ISBN 0 435 53582 X

Designed and typeset by Tech-Set Ltd., Gateshead, Tyne and Wear

Original illustrations © Harcourt Education Limited, 2003

Cover design by Miller, Craig and Cocking

Printed in the United Kingdom by Scotprint

Cover photo: © Stone Picture Library

Acknowledgements
Every effort has been made to contact copyright holders of material reproduced in this book. Any ommissions will be rectified in subsequent printings if notice is given to the publishers.

The answers are not the responsibility of Edexcel.

Publishing team	Design	Production	Editorial
Author team	Phil Richards	David Lawrence	Naomi Anderson
Karen Hughes	Colette Jacquelin	Jason Wyatt	Sue Bennett
Trevor Johnson			Lauren Bourque
Peter Jolly			Des Brady
David Kent			John Deans
Keith Pledger			Nicholas Georgiou
			Amanda Halden
			Maggie Rumble

Tel: 01865 888058 www.heinemann.co.uk

About this book

This book provides a substantial bank of additional exercises to complement those in the Edexcel GCSE Modular Mathematics Examples and Practice book (Intermediate Stage 1) and offers a firm foundation for a programme of consolidation and homework.

Extra exercises are included for every topic covered in the course textbook.

An exam-style practice paper at the back of the book will help you make sure that you are totally exam-ready. This paper is exactly the same length and standard as your actual Stage 1 exam.

Clear links to the course textbook exercises help you plan your use of the book:

Exercise 1A	Links 1A

This exercise is linked to exercise 1A in the Examples and Practice book (Intermediate Stage 1).

Please note that the answers to the questions are provided in a separate booklet, available free when you order a pack of 10 practice books. You can buy further copies direct from Heinemmann Customer Services.

Also available from Heinemann:

Edexcel GCSE Modular Mathematics:
Intermediate Stage 2
Intermediate Stage 3

Contents

1 Integers and powers

1 From each list of numbers, write down the integers:
   (a) 7, 0.7, 70, −7, −0.7, −70
   (b) 31, −3.1, 0.31, 310, 0.031
   (c) $4\frac{1}{2}$, 0, 45, −450, −4.5

2 Write the following numbers in words:
   (a) 926   **(b)** 7014
   (c) 8070   **(d)** 23 604
   (e) 501 279   **(f)** 658 090
   (g) 2 438 671   **(h)** 7 951 002

3 Write the following numbers in digits:
   (a) seven hundred and nineteen
   (b) eight thousand and twelve
   (c) twenty four thousand and twelve
   (d) two hundred and sixteen thousand and eight
   (e) five million, two hundred and eighty thousand and sixty
   (f) three quarters of a million.

Do not use a calculator for this exercise.

1 Work out:
   (a) 372×14 **(b)** 275×31
   (c) 673×47 **(d)** 487×66
   (e) 109×83 **(f)** 704×61

2 Work out:
   (a) $432 \div 12$ **(b)** $912 \div 19$
   (c) $705 \div 15$ **(d)** $644 \div 23$
   (e) $576 \div 24$ **(f)** $806 \div 26$

Do not use a calculator for this exercise.

1 Work out:
   (a) $8 + -5$ **(b)** $7 - +8$ **(c)** $5 - -6$ **(d)** $-4 + +5$
   (e) $-4 - -3$ **(f)** $-6 + -3$ **(g)** $-1 - +7$ **(h)** $-6 + +6$

2 Work out:
 (a) 4×-5 (b) -6×-3 (c) $-28 \div -7$
 (d) $-32 \div 4$ (e) -2×7 (f) -9×0
 (g) $35 \div -5$ (h) -8×-5

3 The temperature inside an aircraft is $18\,^\circ\text{C}$ and the temperature outside is $-48\,^\circ\text{C}$.
 (a) Find the difference between these temperatures.
 When the aircraft climbs, the outside temperature falls by $6\,^\circ\text{C}$.
 (b) Find the new outside temperature.

Exercise 1D   Links 1D

1 Write the following numbers correct to 1 significant figure:
 (a) 23   (b) 453   (c) 8.6   (d) 65
 (e) 4712   (f) 23.9   (g) 8396   (h) 950

2 For each of the following calculations:
 (i) write down a calculation that can be used to estimate the answer,
 (ii) work out an estimate for the answer.

> Do not use a calculator for this question.

  (a) 23×48 (b) $59 \div 31$ (c) 436×63

  (d) $592 \div 187$ (e) $\dfrac{832 \times 18}{169}$ (f) $\dfrac{550 \times 42}{36 \times 25}$

3 A car travels 42 miles on one gallon of petrol. Work out an estimate for the distance it will travel on 56 gallons.

4 A cereal bar weighs 27 grams. Work out an estimate for the weight of 18 of these cereal bars.

5 Each person in a theatre audience paid £25 for a ticket. The total income from ticket sales was £9450. Work out an estimate for the number of people in the audience.

Exercise 1E   Links 1E

1 Write down all the square numbers between 40 and 90.

2 Write down both the cube numbers between 200 and 500.

3 1 is both a square number and a cube number. Find another number, below 100, which is both a square number and a cube number.

4 Write down the value of:
  (a) the square of 31   **(b)** the cube of 12
  (c) 5.3^2 **(d)** 2.9^3
  (e) the positive square root of 676
  (f) $\sqrt{225}$ **(g)** the cube root of 216
  (h) $\sqrt[3]{-729}$ **(i)** the negative square root of 1.44
  (j) the square of -2.8 **(k)** $\sqrt{0.81}$
  (l) $\sqrt[3]{59.319}$ **(m)** 0.3 squared
  (n) $(-0.7)^2$

5 The cube of a number is **not** always greater than the square of the same number. Give an example to show this.

Exercise 1F   Links 1F

1 Work out:
  (a) $8 - 2 \times 3$ **(b)** $5 + 12 \div 3$
  (c) $(8 + 3) - (6 - 1)$ **(d)** $(9 - 2) \times 5$
  (e) $\dfrac{9 \times 4}{7 + 5}$ **(f)** $20 - 4^2$
  (g) $(8 - 3)^2$ **(h)** $\sqrt{(9 + 16)}$
  (i) $\sqrt{9} + \sqrt{16}$ **(j)** $\dfrac{\sqrt{100}}{3^2 + 1}$
  (k) $(2 - 7)^2 \times 3$ **(l)** $\dfrac{(4 \times 5)^2}{4 \times 5^2}$

2 Make these expressions correct by replacing the * with $+$, $-$, $\times$ or $\div$. Use brackets if you need to.
  (a) $4 * 7 * 2 = 26$ **(b)** $4 * 7 * 2 = 20$
  (c) $3 * 2 * 6 = 30$ **(d)** $3 * 2 * 6 = 15$
  (e) $5 * 4 * 9 * 1 = 40$ **(f)** $5 * 4 * 9 * 1 = 80$
  (g) $5 * 4 * 9 * 1 = 72$ **(h)** $5 * 4 * 9 * 1 = 37$
  (i) $24 * 3 * 5 = 13$ **(j)** $24 * 3 * 5 = 3$

Exercise 1G   Links 1G

1 Write down all the factors of:
  (a) 20   **(b)** 32   **(c)** 35   **(d)** 37   **(e)** 55

2 Write down all the prime factors of:
  (a) 15   **(b)** 18   **(c)** 21   **(d)** 60   **(e)** 70

3 Write down the first 5 multiples of:
  (a) 9   **(b)** 12

4 Write the following in prime factor form (simplify your answers):
(a) 40   **(b)** 60   **(c)** 225   **(d)** 84   **(e)** 150

5 Write down four numbers, each of which has 2 and 3 as its **only** prime factors.

6 Find the HCF of:
(a) 10 and 15   **(b)** 12 and 30   **(c)** 27 and 45
(d) 8, 12 and 28   **(e)** 24, 36 and 60.

7 Find the LCM of:
(a) 10 and 15   **(b)** 6 and 21   **(c)** 7 and 11
(d) 4, 6 and 9   **(e)** 5, 6 and 8.

8 In prime factor form, two numbers are $2^2 \times 3$ and $2 \times 3^2 \times 5$. Find, as ordinary numbers, the HCF and the LCM of the two numbers.

Exercise 1H Mixed questions   Links 1H

1 Write down the integers from this list of numbers:
$$2, \quad -2, \quad 0.2, \quad 0, \quad 20, \quad 0.02$$

2 Write the number 40 030 in words.

Do not use a calculator for questions **2–6**.

3 Write the following numbers in digits:
(a) six million, thirty two thousand and four
(b) two and a half million.

4 Work out:
(a) 439×18 **(b)** 608×53
(c) $752 \div 16$ **(d)** $702 \div 27$

5 Work out:
(a) $5 + -8$ **(b)** $-2 - -7$
(c) -7×-3 **(d)** $32 \div -4$

6 For each of the following calculations:
  (i) write down a calculation that can be used to estimate the answer,
  (ii) work out an estimate for the answer.

(a) 37×68 **(b)** $286 \div 54$ **(c)** $\dfrac{3825}{23 \times 46}$

7 Write down two prime numbers whose sum is a square number.

8 Write down the value of:
(a) 19^2 **(b)** 2.7^3 **(c)** $\sqrt{1156}$
(d) $\sqrt[3]{-5.832}$ **(e)** the positive square root of 0.64

9 Use BIDMAS to work out the value of:

(a) $8 + 5 \times 2$ **(b)** $20 - (7 - 3)^2$ **(c)** $\dfrac{6^2 + 6 \times 2}{(3 + 1) \times 3}$

Do not use a calculator for question **9**.

10 Write 270 as a product of its prime factors.

11 Express 300 as a product of its prime factors.

12 **(a)** Find the highest common factor (HCF) of 24 and 30.
(b) Find the lowest common multiple (LCM) of 24 and 30.

2 Fractions and decimals

1 Copy and complete these sets of equivalent fractions:

(a) $\dfrac{5}{6} = \dfrac{}{12} = \dfrac{}{18} = \dfrac{}{24}$ (b) $\dfrac{7}{8} = \dfrac{21}{} = \dfrac{}{40} = \dfrac{49}{}$

2 Copy and complete:

(a) $\dfrac{2}{9} = \dfrac{}{36}$ (b) $\dfrac{7}{10} = \dfrac{42}{}$ (c) $\dfrac{5}{12} = \dfrac{}{84}$

3 Write each fraction in its simplest form:
(a) $\dfrac{8}{10}$ (b) $\dfrac{12}{15}$ (c) $\dfrac{20}{35}$ (d) $\dfrac{27}{36}$
(e) $\dfrac{18}{48}$ (f) $\dfrac{16}{36}$ (g) $\dfrac{24}{32}$ (h) $\dfrac{45}{50}$

1 Change each mixed number to an improper fraction:
(a) $1\frac{1}{5}$ (b) $1\frac{5}{6}$ (c) $2\frac{4}{5}$ (d) $2\frac{5}{9}$
(e) $3\frac{7}{8}$ (f) $4\frac{9}{10}$ (g) $6\frac{1}{2}$ (h) $5\frac{3}{8}$

2 Change each improper fraction to a mixed number in its simplest form:
(a) $\dfrac{11}{2}$ (b) $\dfrac{19}{4}$ (c) $\dfrac{16}{6}$ (d) $\dfrac{48}{9}$
(e) $\dfrac{76}{10}$ (f) $\dfrac{27}{5}$ (g) $\dfrac{38}{7}$ (h) $\dfrac{33}{12}$

In this exercise, write each answer in its simplest form. Do not use a calculator.

1 Work out:
(a) $\frac{2}{9} + \frac{4}{9}$ (b) $\frac{7}{12} - \frac{5}{12}$ (c) $\frac{4}{5} + \frac{3}{10}$ (d) $\frac{5}{7} - \frac{1}{3}$
(e) $\frac{5}{6} + \frac{3}{4}$ (f) $\frac{7}{12} - \frac{3}{8}$ (g) $\frac{4}{5} + \frac{2}{3}$ (h) $\frac{11}{15} - \frac{13}{20}$

2 Work out:
(a) $2\frac{1}{2} + \frac{3}{4}$ (b) $3\frac{4}{5} + 1\frac{7}{10}$ (c) $2\frac{1}{3} + 3\frac{2}{5}$ (d) $2\frac{3}{10} + 1\frac{5}{6}$
(e) $4\frac{5}{8} + 1\frac{7}{12}$ (f) $2\frac{3}{4} + 2\frac{1}{3}$ (g) $3\frac{1}{6} + 2\frac{5}{9}$ (h) $3\frac{2}{5} + 2\frac{3}{4}$

3 Work out:
   (a) $1\frac{7}{8} - \frac{3}{4}$ **(b)** $3\frac{7}{10} - 1\frac{2}{5}$ **(c)** $2\frac{4}{5} - 1\frac{1}{2}$ **(d)** $3\frac{5}{8} - 1\frac{3}{10}$
   (e) $4\frac{1}{6} - \frac{2}{3}$ **(f)** $2\frac{1}{2} - 1\frac{3}{5}$ **(g)** $4\frac{2}{5} - 1\frac{3}{4}$ **(h)** $2\frac{5}{12} - 1\frac{7}{9}$

4

●━━━━━━━●━━━━━━━━━━●━━━━━━━━━━━━━━━━━━●
Exit   Exit   Leatherhead   Dorking
sign

Hayley passed an exit sign showing the distance to the next motorway exit as $\frac{1}{3}$ mile. She left the motorway at that exit and then drove on to Leatherhead. The distance from the exit to Leatherhead is $1\frac{3}{4}$ miles.

(a) Work out the distance from the exit sign to Leatherhead.
She drove further along the same road to Dorking.
The distance from the **exit** to Dorking is $7\frac{1}{2}$ miles.
(b) Work out the distance between Leatherhead and Dorking.

Exercise 2D   Links 2D

Write every answer in this exercise in its simplest form. Do not use a calculator.

1 Work out:
   (a) $\frac{1}{4} \times \frac{5}{6}$ **(b)** $\frac{2}{3} \div \frac{5}{7}$ **(c)** $\frac{3}{5} \times \frac{4}{9}$
   (d) $\frac{3}{8} \div \frac{4}{5}$ **(e)** $\frac{5}{6} \div \frac{7}{12}$ **(f)** $\frac{9}{16} \times \frac{8}{9}$

2 Work out:
   (a) $1\frac{3}{4} \times \frac{1}{3}$ **(b)** $2\frac{1}{2} \times 1\frac{1}{6}$ **(c)** $1\frac{2}{3} \times 2\frac{3}{5}$
   (d) $3\frac{2}{3} \times 1\frac{4}{5}$ **(e)** $9 \times \frac{3}{8}$ **(f)** $2\frac{5}{6} \times 3$

3 Work out:
   (a) $1\frac{1}{3} \div \frac{3}{5}$ **(b)** $2\frac{1}{3} \div 1\frac{3}{4}$ **(c)** $2\frac{4}{5} \div 3\frac{1}{2}$
   (d) $6 \div \frac{4}{5}$ **(e)** $\frac{2}{3} \div 5$ **(f)** $2\frac{2}{5} \div 6$

4 Paul works for $7\frac{3}{4}$ hours each day for five days. For how long does he work altogether?

5 1 kilogram is approximately the same as $2\frac{1}{5}$ pounds.
   (a) Convert $\frac{3}{4}$ kilogram to pounds.
   (b) Convert $3\frac{1}{2}$ kilograms to pounds.
   (c) Convert $5\frac{1}{2}$ pounds to kilograms.

6 The wine in a $\frac{3}{4}$ litre bottle is poured into six glasses with an equal amount of wine in each glass. Work out, as a fraction of a litre, the amount of wine in each glass.

Exercise 2E   Links 2E

Do not use a calculator for this exercise.

1   Write down the answers to:
   (a) 6.7×10 (b) $37.1 \div 10$
   (c) 4.92×100 (d) $2.9 \div 100$
   (e) 0.83×1000 (f) $476.5 \div 1000$
   (g) 26.7×100 (h) $0.71 \div 1000$

2   One can holds 0.33 litres of cola. How many litres of cola do
    ten of these cans hold?

3   100 grams of yoghurt contains 4.4 grams of fat. Work out the
    weight, in grams, of fat in 1 gram of yoghurt.

4   How many centimetres are there in 3.62 metres? (1 m = 100 cm.)

Exercise 2F   Links 2F

1   Rearrange each of these lists of numbers in ascending order:
   (a) 0.1, 0.09, 0.01, 0.91, 0.19
   (b) 4.7, 4.07, 4.69, 4.071, 4.069
   (c) 2.45, 2.5, 2.54, 2.545, 2.445
   (d) 0.08, 0.8, 0.79, 0.078, 0.081

2   The depths of snow, in metres, on the slopes of 5 ski resorts
    on one day are shown below:

Aspen	0.95
Cortina	1.05
Klosters	1.85
Tignes	1.55
Zermatt	1.80

   Rearrange the list of depths in ascending order.

3   Here are the distances, in metres, 6 women threw a javelin:
              61.09   60.19   59.98   60.91   60.90   61.01
   Rearrange the list of distances in descending order.

Exercise 2G   Links 2G

Do not use a calculator for this exercise.

1   Work out:
   (a) 8×0.7 (b) 0.06×0.8
   (c) 4.3×0.9 (d) 0.51×8.3
   (e) 23.7×3.6 (f) 9.62×0.073
   (g) 3.8×21.4 (h) 5.29×61

2 Work out:
   (a) $19.2 \div 3$ (b) $87.5 \div 5$
   (c) $28.2 \div 5$ (d) $4.76 \div 0.7$
   (e) $3.212 \div 0.4$ (f) $35.4 \div 1.5$
   (g) $2.01 \div 0.24$ (h) $0.678 \div 0.012$

3 Kate travels 12.7 km on her journey to work. Work out the total distance she travels on six of these journeys.

4 Tom shares £65.48 equally among his four children. How much does each child receive?

5 When Sam completes one lap of a running track, she covers 0.4 km. How many laps must she complete to cover 10 km?

Exercise 2H   Links 2H

1 Change these fractions into decimals:
   (a) $\frac{1}{4}$ (b) $\frac{3}{8}$ (c) $\frac{7}{9}$ (d) $\frac{13}{20}$ (e) $\frac{5}{6}$
   (f) $\frac{17}{25}$ (g) $\frac{5}{11}$ (h) $\frac{3}{16}$ (i) $\frac{5}{12}$ (j) $\frac{13}{22}$

2 Change these decimals into fractions. Simplify your answers if possible.
   (a) 0.9   (b) 0.8   (c) 0.68   (d) 0.31   (e) 0.85
   (f) 0.06   (g) 0.145 (h) 0.268   (i) 0.075   (j) 0.009

3 (a) Find a decimal with one decimal place, the value of which is between $\frac{1}{6}$ and $\frac{2}{9}$.
   (b) Convert your decimal to a fraction in its simplest form.

Exercise 2I   Links 2I

1 Rearrange each list in ascending order:
   (a) $\frac{17}{20}$, 0.82, 0.9, $\frac{4}{5}$, $\frac{21}{25}$ (b) $4\frac{7}{100}$, 4.06, $4\frac{3}{40}$, 4.03, $4\frac{1}{20}$
   (c) 0.78, $\frac{7}{9}$, 0.77, $\frac{3}{4}$, $\frac{19}{25}$ (d) $\frac{16}{25}$, $\frac{2}{3}$, $\frac{5}{8}$, $\frac{7}{11}$, $\frac{13}{20}$

2 The numbers in this list are in ascending order.
$$\frac{7}{13} \quad x \quad \frac{6}{11} \quad \frac{4}{7} \quad y \quad \frac{7}{12}$$
   x and y are decimals with two decimal places. Find x and y.

Exercise 2J Mixed questions   Links 2J

1 Copy and complete:

   (a) $\dfrac{2}{3} = \dfrac{}{27}$ (b) $\dfrac{4}{5} = \dfrac{24}{}$ (c) $\dfrac{3}{7} = \dfrac{}{28}$

2 Write each fraction in its simplest form:

    (a) $\frac{15}{18}$ **(b)** $\frac{21}{35}$ **(c)** $\frac{18}{24}$ **(d)** $\frac{32}{56}$

3 Change each mixed number to an improper fraction:

    (a) $1\frac{5}{8}$ **(b)** $3\frac{2}{9}$ **(c)** $4\frac{3}{10}$ **(d)** $7\frac{5}{6}$

4 Change each improper fraction to a mixed number in its simplest form:

    (a) $\frac{17}{3}$ **(b)** $\frac{44}{5}$ **(c)** $\frac{40}{6}$ **(d)** $\frac{68}{10}$

5 Work out:

> Do not use a calculator for questions **5–11**.

    (a) $\frac{3}{5}+\frac{5}{6}$ **(b)** $\frac{5}{8}-\frac{7}{12}$ **(c)** $1\frac{2}{3}+2\frac{1}{5}$

    (d) $4\frac{1}{2}+1\frac{2}{7}$ **(e)** $2\frac{7}{9}+3\frac{2}{3}$ **(f)** $3\frac{3}{4}-1\frac{9}{10}$

6 Work out:

    (a) $\frac{5}{12}\times\frac{9}{10}$ **(b)** $\frac{7}{8}\div\frac{11}{12}$ **(c)** $3\frac{1}{2}\times2\frac{2}{7}$

    (d) $3\frac{2}{3}\div2\frac{1}{5}$ **(e)** $2\frac{3}{8}\times2\frac{2}{3}$ **(f)** $1\frac{4}{5}\div2\frac{1}{10}$

7 1 kilometre is approximately the same as $\frac{5}{8}$ mile.

    (a) Convert $\frac{2}{5}$ kilometre to miles.

    (b) Convert $2\frac{4}{5}$ kilometres to miles.

8 Write down the answers to:

    (a) 27.4×10 **(b)** $9.81\div10$ **(c)** 2.9×100

    (d) $3.68\div100$ **(e)** 8.4×1000 **(f)** $27.4\div1000$

9 100 grams of Wheat Flakes contain 1.2 grams of protein. Work out the weight, in grams, of protein in:

    (a) 1 gram of Wheat Flakes,

    (b) 1 kilogram of Wheat Flakes. (1 kg = 1000 g.)

10 Work out:

    (a) 2.7×6.39 **(b)** $8.46\div1.8$

    (c) 0.29×23.7 **(d)** $0.783\div0.09$

11 1 centimetre is approximately the same as 0.394 inches. Convert 2.7 cm to inches.

12 Change these fractions into decimals:

    (a) $\frac{17}{20}$ **(b)** $\frac{9}{11}$ **(c)** $\frac{21}{25}$ **(d)** $\frac{11}{15}$

13 Change these decimals into fractions in their simplest forms:

    (a) 0.29   **(b)** 0.55   **(c)** 0.275   **(d)** 0.046

14 Rearrange this list of fractions in ascending order:

$$\frac{9}{20} \qquad \frac{4}{9} \qquad \frac{12}{25} \qquad \frac{5}{11} \qquad \frac{6}{13}$$

15 Rearrange this list of numbers in descending order:

$$0.715 \qquad \frac{11}{15} \qquad \frac{18}{25} \qquad \frac{5}{7} \qquad 0.71$$

3 Percentages

1 Write these percentages as (i) decimals (ii) fractions:
   (a) 50%   (b) 30%   (c) 15%   (d) 48%
   (e) 47%   (f) $72\frac{1}{2}\%$ (g) $11\frac{1}{4}\%$ (h) $10\frac{1}{2}\%$
   (i) $87\frac{1}{2}\%$ (j) $16\frac{2}{3}\%$ (k) $15\frac{1}{4}\%$ (l) $2\frac{1}{3}\%$

2 Write as percentages:
   (a) $\frac{1}{4}$ (b) 0.5   (c) 0.24   (d) $\frac{7}{40}$
   (e) 0.72   (f) $\frac{3}{5}$ (g) 0.685   (h) $\frac{19}{40}$
   (i) 0.0335   (j) $\frac{5}{6}$ (k) 0.38   (l) 0.17

3 Copy and complete the table:

Fraction	Decimal	Percentage
		25%
$\frac{9}{10}$		
	0.24	
$\frac{4}{5}$		
	0.74	
$\frac{7}{8}$		
		$66\frac{2}{3}\%$

4 Write these in order. Start with the smallest.

     0.17, $\frac{8}{50}$,   0.018,   12%, $\frac{1}{8}$

5 Write 11 out of 25 as a percentage.

1 Work out:
   (a) 20% of 50   (b) 30% of 60   (c) 45% of 20
   (d) 25% of 32   (e) 24% of £20   (f) 72% of £30
   (g) 27% of £50   (h) $33\frac{1}{3}\%$ of £60   (i) $57\frac{1}{2}\%$ of 500 g
   (j) $66\frac{2}{3}\%$ of £54   (k) $17\frac{1}{2}\%$ of £200   (l) $17\frac{1}{2}\%$ of 1000 kg.

2 Jessie earns £21 000 a year.
   She pays 23% tax.
   How much tax does Jessie pay?

3 In a school there are 160 pupils in Year 10.
Boys make up $52\frac{1}{2}\%$ of the pupils in Year 10. Find:
(a) the number of boys in Year 10,
(b) the number of girls in Year 10.

4 Emma buys a box of 30 pens for £4.50.
She sells the pens for 20p each.
She sells all the pens.
Work out her percentage profit.

5 The population of a country is 30 million.
8% of the population are over 70.
Work out how many of the population are over 70.

6 A book costs £16.
The author is paid $12\frac{1}{2}\%$ of the cost of the book.
Work out how much the author receives from each book sold.

7 A hotel has 144 rooms.
37.5% of the rooms are empty.
Work out the number of rooms in the hotel which are **not** empty.

Exercise 3C	Links 3C

1 The advertised price of a van is

$$£6000 + VAT$$

The rate of VAT is $17\frac{1}{2}\%$. Work out the total cost of the van.

2 The cost of a new house in 2002 was £150 000.
The house sold in 2003 for a profit of 18%.
Work out the cost of the house in 2003.

3 Joe puts £500 into a saving account on 1 January 2003. The money in the savings account earns 5% interest per year. How much does Joe have in the account on 1 January 2004?

4

> ### DVD player
> ### £190 + VAT at $17\frac{1}{2}\%$

Calculate the cost of a DVD player.

5 Steven bought a new car for £12 000.
The car depreciated by 45% over 3 years.
Work out the value of Steven's car after 3 years.

6 Roy buys some slabs for his patio. The normal cost of these slabs is £560.
Roy is given a 12% discount if he pays in cash.
Roy pays in cash.
Work out how much he pays.

7 Alison was earning £16 000 per year.
She received a 7% rise in her pay.
Work out her earnings per year after the pay rise.

Exercise 3D   Links 3D

1 Andy scored 32 out of 40 in a numeracy test.
Write this as a percentage.

2 A car manufacturer increases their prices.
Before the increase, the price of a new car was £10 200.
After the increase, the same car cost £10 608.
Calculate the percentage increase in price of the car.

3 A bed cost £400 to make.
It was sold for £700.
Work out the percentage profit.

4 A bag contains 20 chocolates.
11 are plain, 5 are milk and 4 are white.
(a) What percentage of all the chocolates are plain?
Mandy eats all the plain chocolates but she eats none of the others.
(b) Write the number of white chocolates as a percentage of the number of milk chocolates.

5 The normal cost of a skirt is £40. It is sold in the sale for £28.
Calculate the percentage reduction in its price.

6 Alan bought a box of paper which had extra sheets free. The number of sheets had increased from 80 to 100. Calculate the percentage increase in the number of sheets.

7 The cost of a CD player fell from £220 to £182.
Calculate the percentage decrease in the cost of the CD player.

Exercise 3E Mixed questions   Links 3E

1 Lesley's mark in a Geography test was 48 out of 60.
Work out 48 out of 60 as a percentage.   (L)

2 Lisa had £10.50.
She gave 8% to charity and kept the rest of her money.
Work out how much money she kept. (L)

3 Mrs Brown bought 32 pens for a total of £11.20.
She sold all of the pens.
She made a profit of 20% on each pen.
Work out how much she sold each pen for. (L)

4 The population of a city is 8 million.
9% of the population are senior citizens.
Work out 9% of 8 million. (L)

5 A hotel has 72 rooms.
37.5% of the rooms are empty.
Work out the number of rooms that are not empty.

6 Jack buys a box of 20 pens for £3.00.
He sells the pens for 21p each.
He sells all the pens.
Work out his percentage profit. (L)

7 Write 11 out of 25 as a percentage. (L)

8 Work out 20% of £1800. (L)

9 $30\%, \frac{1}{4}, 0.35, \frac{1}{3}, \frac{2}{5}, 0.299$
Write this list of six numbers in order of size.
Start with the smallest. (L)

10 Write these numbers in order of size.
Start with the largest.

$$0.8 \qquad 70\% \qquad \frac{7}{8} \qquad \frac{3}{4}$$ (L)

11 The rate of simple interest is 4% per year.
Work out the simple interest paid on £500 in 3 years. (L)

12 Jane is going to buy a computer for £680 + 17% VAT.
Work out the total price, including VAT, that Jane will pay for the computer. (L)

13 The total cost of orange drink for 50 cups is £7.50.
Each cup of drink is sold at a 20% profit.
Work out the price at which each cup of orange drink is sold. (L)

14 In a sale all the prices are reduced by 30%.
The sale price of a jacket is £28.
Work out the price of the jacket before the sale. (L)

15 Joe got 36 out of 80 in an English test.
(a) Work out 36 out of 80 as a percentage.
Jo got 65% of the total number of marks in a French test.
Jo got 39 marks.
(b) Work out the total number of marks for the French test.

4 Coordinates and the elements of algebra

1 Plot the points A (2, 1), B (5, 2) and C (3, 4).
Draw the triangle ABC.

2 Plot the coordinates P (−1, −1), Q (3, 0), R (2, 4) and S (−2, 3).
Draw the shape $PQRS$.
Name the shape $PQRS$.

3 Draw the following axes:
x-axis from −6 to 6.
y-axis from −6 to 6.
Plot the points A (−1, −2) and B (3, 1).
The points C and D are such that $ABCD$ is a square.
Find the possible coordinates of C and D.

4 Draw the x-axis from −3 to 8.
Draw the y-axis from −3 to 8.
Plot the points A (0, 4), B (6, 3) and C (4, 0).
Write down the coordinates of the point D so that $ABCD$ is a parallelogram.

5 Plot the points P (−1, −2), Q (−3, 2) R (−1, 2) and S (1, −2).
Name the shape $PQRS$.
Write down:
(a) the equation of the line QR,
(b) the equation of the line PR.

6 Plot the points A (1, 1), B (2, 4), C (−2, 4) and D (−1, 1).
Draw $ABCD$.
Name the shape $ABCD$.

7 Plot the points P (−1, −1), Q (2, 2) and R (−1, 2).
Draw the triangle PQR.
Work out the area of PQR.

8 Plot the points A (1, 1) and B (1, 6).
Plot the points C (−2, −2) and D (−2, 3).
Work out:
(a) the length of each of the lines AB and CD.
(b) the angle between the two lines.

Exercise 4B   Links 4B

In each question simplify as fully as possible:

1   $3x + 4x - 5y$ 2 $3a + 5b - 4a$
3   $4n - 5m + n$ 4 $6p - 3p + 4q$
5   $5q - 3r - 3q + 2r$ 6 $c + 4d + 7c - d$
7   $ab + ab$ 8 $cd + dc + cd$
9   $4fh + 2fh - 3fh$ 10 $x^2 - x + 2x$
11 $6b^2 - 2b + 4b$ 12 $5d^2 - 2d^2 + 3d$
13 $a^3 + a^2 + a + a^2$ 14 $b^2 + b^2 - 2ab + b^2 - ab$
15 $2ab - b + 3ab - a + b$ 16 $3cd + c + 2cd + d$
17 $4xy - 3x + 2y + xy$ 18 $5xy - 3xy + 7x - 2y$
19 $5p^2q + 4p^2q + 3p$ 20 $8rs^2 + r - s + rs^2 - 5rs^2$

Exercise 4C   Links 4C

Expand and simplify:

1   $2(x + 3) + 4(x + 3)$ 2 $5(2x - 1) + 3(3x + 2)$
3   $4(x + 1) + 5(2x - 3)$ 4 $5(1 - 2x) + 2(3 - x)$
5   $7(4 - x) - 2(3x - 1)$ 6 $4(2 - 3x) + 5(1 - 2x)$
7   $5(2 - 3x) - 3(7 - x)$ 8 $5(x + 2y) + x + y$
9   $4(2x - 1) + 4(4 - 2x)$ 10 $3(2x - 3) - 2(4x + 7)$
11 $3(3x - 2) - 5(3 - x)$ 12 $7(2x - 1) - 3(2x + 1)$
13 $4(2 - x) - 2(x - 2)$ 14 $8(x + 2y) - 4(y + x)$
15 $2(3 - 2x) + 2(2x - 1)$ 16 $2(y - x) + 3(x - y)$
17 $3(1 - 3x) - 3(x - 3)$ 18 $4(y + 2x) - 3(x + 3y)$
19 $4x - 5y + 2(3x - y)$ 20 $5(x + 3y) - 7(x - y)$
21 $x(2y - 1) + 2x(1 + 3y)$ 22 $2x(x + 2y) - 3y(y - x)$
23 $5a(a + b) - b(b - a)$ 24 $4p(p + 3q) - 2q(p + q)$
25 $3a(b + 2a) + 2b(a + 2b)$ 26 $2t(1 - 3t) - t(4 + 2t)$
27 $4a(a + 2b) - 3b(a - 3b)$ 28 $a(a + b) + b(b + c) + c(a + c)$
29 $b(a - b) - a(a + b)$ 30 $2a(a + 3b) + 3b(a + 2b)$
31 $5b(2a - b) - 2a(3a + b)$ 32 $4x(x - 2y) - 3x(x - 3y)$

Exercise 4D   Links 4D

Factorize:

1   $3x + 15$ 2 $7x - 28$ 3 $15x + 10$
4   $9x - 21$ 5 $5x + 10$ 6 $9x + 15$

7 $18x + 12$ **8** $42 - 30p$ **9** $15 + 30y$

10 $35x + 15$ **11** $8p + 12$ **12** $20x + 30y$

13 $12x - 6y$ **14** $5q + 10p$ **15** $8a - 64b$

16 $18p + 54$ **17** $4a + 6b$ **18** $8a^2 - 128ab$

19 $x^2 - 7xy$ **20** $5a^2 - 15a$ **21** $4p^2 - 8pq$

22 $5ab + a^2$ **23** $7p^2 - 14p$ **24** $6x^3y - 12xy^3$

25 $3ab + 5ac$ **26** $6st - 3s$ **27** $5p^2q - 20pq^2$

28 $8p^2 - 4pq$ **29** $4p^2 + 6p$ **30** $ab^2 - a^2b$

31 $8a^2 - 6abc$ **32** $2x^3 - 4x^2y$ **33** $4p^3q - 8pq^3$

34 $5pq^2 - 10p^2q$ **35** $x^2y - xy^2$ **36** $15ab - 10bc$

Exercise 4E   Links 4E

Select the correct word from 'equation', 'formula', 'identity' and 'expression' to describe each of the following.

1 $3x + 2 = 17$ **2** $8 = 7 + 2x$

3 $5 - 2x = 8$ **4** $12 + 4x$

5 $13 + 3x$ **6** $7x + 2 = 5 + 6x$

7 $p = 3at$ **8** $3pq$

9 $v = 8ut$ **10** $4x(x - 1) = 4x^2 - 4x$

11 $2p^2q$ **12** $y = a + 3x$

13 $3x(x + 3) = 3x^2 + 9x$ **14** $3x - 1$

15 $2y(3y - 1) = 6y^2 - 2y$ **16** $3ab + 4ac = a(3b + 4c)$

17 $x = y + 2z - 3p$ **18** $3(x - 2) = 3x - 6$

19 $2p + 2q$ **20** $3x - 1 = x + 7$

Exercise 4F   Links 4F

1 A car costs

   £p per week to hire
   and £x per gallon for the petrol.

   Joe hires the car for 3 weeks and uses 20 gallons of petrol.
   Write down the formula for the cost.

2 $v = u + at$ is a formula for working out the speed of an object.
   Find v when:
   (a) $u = 10$, $a = 8$ and $t = 4$,
   (b) $u = 3$, $a = -12$ and $t = 2$.

3   The cost, £C, of taking a adults, c children and p old-age pensioners on a day trip is:

$$C = 15a + 5c + 4p$$

Work out the cost of taking:
(a) 5 adults, 20 children and 2 pensioners,
(b) 2 adults, 40 children and 5 pensioners.

4   The formula for the volume of a cylinder is

$$V = \pi r^2 h$$

Work out the volume of a cylinder when:
(a) $r = 10\,\text{cm}, h = 4\,\text{cm}$
(b) $r = 5\,\text{cm}, h = 20\,\text{cm}$
(c) $r = 6\,\text{cm}, h = 10\,\text{cm}$
(d) $r = 10\,\text{cm}, h = 20\,\text{cm}$
(e) $r = h = 15\,\text{cm}.$

5   The formula for the volume of a sphere is

$$V = \tfrac{4}{3}\pi r^3$$

Work out V when:
(a) $r = 2\,\text{cm}$
(b) $r = 5\,\text{cm}.$
Work out r when:
(c) $V = 500\,\text{cm}^3$
(d) $V = 1200\,\text{cm}^3.$

Exercise 4G Mixed questions   Links 4G

1   Simplify fully:
   (a) $a + 5a$ **(b)** $4b - 2b + 5b$
   (c) $3c - 2d + c - d$ **(d)** $6r - 2s - 5s - r$
   (e) $3x + 5y - x + y$ **(f)** $5h + 3g - g - h$

2   Expand:
   (a) $4(3x - 2y)$ **(b)** $b^2(b + ab)$
   (c) $3a(b - 2c)$ **(d)** $3x(2y + 4x)$
   (e) $5pq(p + q)$ **(f)** $4z(2wz - 1)$

3   Factorize:
   (a) $15x - 20$ **(b)** $9p^2 + 6p$
   (c) $4a + 6$ **(d)** $a^3 b - 2ab^3$
   (e) $15p^2 q - 3pq^2$ **(f)** $x^3 + x^2 + x$

4   $v^2 = u^2 + 2fs$ is a formula used in science.
Work out:
   (a) v when $u = 10, f = -5$ and $s = 8,$
   (b) v when $u = -8, f = 6$ and $s = 5.$
Work out:
   (c) u when $v = 5, f = 10$ and $s = -6.$

5 Select the word from the list below which describes each of the following:

$$equation \quad formula \quad expression \quad identity$$

(a) $A = xy$ (b) $4 - 3x = 5x + 2$

(c) $V = \dfrac{M}{D}$ (d) $2\pi(a + b)$

(e) $x(3x - y) = 3x^2 - xy$ (f) $\pi r^2 a$

6 $C = \pi r + 2h.$
Work out:
(a) C when $r = 3\,\text{cm}$ and $h = 5\,\text{cm}$,
(b) r when $h = 8\,\text{cm}$ and $C = 22\,\text{cm}$.

7 Plot the points $A\,(5, 0)$, $B\,(4, 3)$, $C\,(3, 4)$ and $D\,(0, 5)$.
Find four other points which are the same distance from the origin as each of A, B, C and D.

5 Algebraic equations

Exercise 5A   Links 5A

Solve these equations using inverse operations.

1 $a + 8 = 14$ **2** $6b = 24$ **3** $\dfrac{c}{4} = 5$

4 $3d + 7 = 19$ **5** $5e - 4 = 21$ **6** $\dfrac{f - 2}{8} = 3$

7 $3(g + 4) = 27$ **8** $\dfrac{p}{3} + 2 = 14$ **9** $\dfrac{m + 2}{5} = 2$

10 $2(n - 3) = 4$ **11** $4p + 2 = 16$ **12** $\dfrac{q + 6}{3} = 1$

13 $\dfrac{t}{4} + 6 = 6$ **14** $15v - 2 = 3$ **15** $4(x + 5) = 9$

16 $3(y - 4) = 2$ **17** $\dfrac{a}{5} + 7 = 5$ **18** $10b + 4 = 4$

19 $4(3c + 1) = 28$ **20** $\dfrac{5d + 16}{3} = 2$

Exercise 5B   Links 5B

Solve these equations using the balance method.

1 $a - 3 = 11$ **2** $7b = 21$ **3** $\dfrac{c}{3} = 4$

4 $4d - 2 = 14$ **5** $2(e + 4) = 12$ **6** $\dfrac{f + 3}{2} = 4$

7 $6g + 3 = 27$ **8** $\dfrac{h}{4} - 3 = 1$ **9** $5(m - 2) = 20$

10 $\dfrac{n - 1}{7} = 2$ **11** $15p - 2 = 1$ **12** $4(q + 3) = 4$

13 $\dfrac{t + 9}{2} = 3$ **14** $3v + 5 = 2$ **15** $\dfrac{x}{4} + 1 = 6$

16 $3(y - 2) = 2$ **17** $6a + 14 = 2$ **18** $4(b - 2) = 10$

19 $\dfrac{4c + 3}{5} = 1$ **20** $4(2d - 3) = -28$

Exercise 5C Links 5C

Solve these equations using the balance method.

1   $4a + 3 = 3a + 7$ 2 $7b - 4 = 4b + 5$

3   $4(c - 2) = 2c + 4$ 4 $6(d + 2) = 4(d + 10)$

5   $5e - 2 = 9e - 10$ 6 $8f + 4 = 5f + 7$

7   $3(g - 2) = 8g + 9$ 8 $7(h - 1) = 4(h - 4)$

9   $2(p + 6) = 5(p - 3)$ 10 $6(q - 4) = 4q + 1$

Exercise 5D Links 5D

Solve these equations using the balance method.

1   $7 - x = 5$ 2 $8 - 3x = 2$

3   $12 - 5x = 2$ 4 $4x + 3 = 9 - x$

5   $3(x + 1) = 12 - 2x$ 6 $10 - 3x = 2x$

7   $11 - 2x = 5x + 2$ 8 $3 - x = 4x - 12$

9   $2 - x = 11 - 2x$ 10 $14 - 2x = 5 - 5x$

11   $6 - 4x = 14 - 2x$ 12 $24 - 3x = 4 - 7x$

13   $2 - 5x = 12$ 14 $4 - 2x = 4$

15   $5 - 3x = -4$ 16 $6 + 3x = 8 - 5x$

17   $10 - 2x = 15 + 3x$ 18 $6(4 - x) = 10 + 2x$

19   $13 - 4x = 6 - 2x$ 20 $15 - 2x = 11 - 5x$

Exercise 5E Links 5E

1   I think of a number. I multiply it by 5 and subtract 2. The result is 28. Find the number.

2   The sizes of the angles of a triangle are $a + 50°$, $a + 30°$ and $a - 10°$. Find the size of the smallest angle of the triangle.

3   I think of a number. I multiply it by 4 and subtract the result from 40. The answer is 16. Find the number.

4   The diagram shows three angles at a point. Find the size of each of the angles.

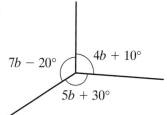

5 The lengths, in centimetres, of four sides of a rectangle are $2x + 3$, $4x - 4$, $17 - 3x$ and $8 - x$. The perimeter of the rectangle is $30\,\text{cm}$. Find the length of each of the sides.

6 The length of each side of a regular pentagon is $2a + 6\,\text{cm}$. The perimeter of the pentagon is $60\,\text{cm}$. Find the value of a.

7 I think of a number. I multiply it by 5 and subtract 4 from the result. The answer is the same as when I multiply the number by 3 and add 12 to the result. Find the number.

8 Graham is 3 times older than his cousin. His cousin is also 18 years younger than him.
Find Graham's age.

9 The length of a rectangle is $6\,\text{cm}$ greater than its width. The perimeter of the rectangle is $48\,\text{cm}$. Find the width of the rectangle.

10

2y + 80°   4x − 60°
3x − 30°   7y − 20°

The diagram shows a parallelogram. Find the values of x and y.

Hint:
Opposite angles of a parallelogram are equal.

Exercise 5F   Links 5F

Solve the following equations.

1 $\dfrac{a}{6} + 1 = \dfrac{a}{5}$

2 $\dfrac{b}{4} + 2 = \dfrac{b}{6} + 4$

3 $\dfrac{c + 4}{3} - 4 = 2$

4 $\dfrac{d}{3} + \dfrac{d}{2} = 10$

5 $\dfrac{4e + 7}{9} = 3$

6 $\dfrac{p}{4} + 4 = \dfrac{p - 2}{2} + 3$

7 $\dfrac{4n - 1}{5} = \dfrac{10n + 5}{3}$

8 $\dfrac{m + 6}{3} = \dfrac{m + 14}{4} - 1$

9 $4(y - 2) = \dfrac{y}{3} + 14$

10 $3(x + 1) = \dfrac{2x - 4}{5} + 22$

11 $\dfrac{q + 2}{4} = \dfrac{q}{3} + 3$

12 $\dfrac{t - 2}{5} + 3 = \dfrac{t}{2} + 9$

13 $\dfrac{6 - 3x}{4} = 3$

14 $\dfrac{18 - 3w}{2} = w + 4$

15 $\dfrac{18 - 3x}{4} = 4 - x$

16 $\dfrac{10 - 2y}{3} = 1 - 3y$

17 $\dfrac{2 - 3x}{3} = \dfrac{x + 1}{2}$

18 $\dfrac{3x - 2}{6} + \dfrac{x + 2}{3} = 2$

19 $\dfrac{4y + 1}{3} + \dfrac{y - 5}{4} = 1$

20 $\dfrac{2x - 3}{5} - \dfrac{3x + 4}{3} = -1$

Exercise 5G   Links 5G

Solve the following equations.

1 $x^2 + 2 = 38$ 2 $x^2 - 5 = 76$ 3 $4x^2 = 64$

4 $6x^2 = 54$ 5 $\dfrac{x^2}{5} = 5$ 6 $5x^2 + 6 = 26$

7 $4x^2 - 3 = 33$ 8 $x^2 = \dfrac{16}{25}$ 9 $x^2 = \dfrac{81}{16}$

10 $9x^2 = 1$ 11 $36x^2 = 16$ 12 $49x^2 = 25$

13 $25x^2 = 1$ 14 $16x^2 = 100$ 15 $81x^2 = 49$

Exercise 5H   Links 5H

Solve the following equations.

1 $\dfrac{36}{a} = 6$ 2 $\dfrac{30}{b} = 5$ 3 $\dfrac{12}{c} = 24$ 4 $\dfrac{7}{d} = 21$

5 $\dfrac{7}{e} = 3$ 6 $\dfrac{3}{q} = 4$ 7 $\dfrac{1}{t} = 7$ 8 $\dfrac{4}{t} = 5$

9 $\dfrac{8}{x} = 5$ 10 $\dfrac{5}{y} = 8$

Exercise 5I Mixed questions   Links 5I

Solve the following equations.

1 $3a - 4 = 11$ 2 $\dfrac{b+8}{7} = 1$

3 $4(c + 3) = 20$ 4 $\dfrac{5d-2}{6} = 3$

5 $7e - 8 = 5e - 2$ 6 $4(f + 3) = 6f + 14$

7 $3(g - 2) = 5(g - 4)$ 8 $9 - 3h = 36$

9 $8m + 9 = 5 - 7m$ 10 $4(6 - 2x) = 6 - 5x$

11 $18 - 7p = 14 - 5p$ 12 $3(5 - 2x) = 3 - 10x$

13 $\dfrac{y}{5} + 2 = \dfrac{y}{10} + 7$ 14 $\dfrac{z-3}{4} = \dfrac{z+1}{2} - 8$

15 $\dfrac{8-3q}{4} = 5$ 16 $\dfrac{19-7t}{4} = 2t + 1$

17 $\dfrac{6-2u}{4} = \dfrac{9-5u}{3}$

18 $\dfrac{7v-2}{3} = \dfrac{2v+5}{4}$

19 $\dfrac{2w+8}{3} - \dfrac{5w+3}{2} = 4$

20 $\dfrac{18}{a} = 3$

21 $\dfrac{5}{b} = 9$

22 $7a^2 + 3 = 25$

23 $16c^2 = 81$

24 The sizes of the angles of a quadrilateral are $4x°$, $2x + 30°$, $3x - 10°$ and $4x - 50°$. Write down the size of the largest angle of the quadrilateral.

25 The length of a rectangle is 5 cm greater than its width. The perimeter of the rectangle is 34 cm. Find its length.

6 Sequences

1 For each of these sequences:
   (a) find the next three terms in the sequence,
   (b) write down the mathematical name for the numbers in the sequence.
      (i) first term = 1; rule is **add 2**
     (ii) first term = 4; rule is **add 4**
    (iii) first term = 3; rule is **multiply by 3**.

2 Find the next three terms in each of these sequences:
   (a) first term = 23; rule is **subtract 3**
   (b) first term = 64; rule is **divide by 4**
   (c) first term = 2; rule is **multiply by 3 then add 1**
   (d) first term = 8; rule is **subtract 3 then multiply by 2**
   (e) first term = 42; rule is **add 4 then divide by 2**.

3 For each of these sequences:
   (a) find the rule for the sequence,
   (b) find the next two terms in the sequence.
      (i) 4, 9, 14, 19, 24, ...
     (ii) 83, 76, 69, 62, 55, ...
    (iii) 2, 8, 32, 128, 512, ...
    (iv) 729, 243, 81, 27, 9, ...

4 For each of these sequences:
   (a) find the next two terms in the sequence,
   (b) write down the mathematical name of the numbers in the sequence.
     (i) 7, 14, 21, 28, 35, ...
    (ii) 5, 25, 125, 625, ...

5 For each of these sequences:
   (a) find the rule for the sequence,
   (b) find the next two terms in the sequence.
      (i) 34, 28, 22, 16, 10, ...
     (ii) 1024, 256, 64, 16, 4, ...
    (iii) −27, −22, −17, −12, −7, ...
    (iv) 81, 27, 9, 3, 1, ...

6 Find the next term for each of these sequences:
   (a) 6, 7, 9, 12, 16, ...   (b) 6, 7, 9, 13, 21, ...
   (c) 3, 7, 15, 27, 43, ...   (d) 3, 33, 59, 81, 99, ...

7 Here are four patterns of dots:

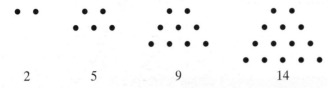

2	5	9	14

  (a) Find the differences for the four patterns of dots.

  (b) Use your answer to (a) to write down a rule for the sequence.

  (c) Use your rule to write down the number of dots in the next four patterns in the sequence.

Exercise 6B   **Links 6B**

---

1 For each of these rules, find:
  (a) the first five terms in the sequence,
  (b) the tenth term of the sequence.
     (i) Multiply the term number by 3 and add 2.
     (ii) Add 3 to the term number and multiply by 3.
     (iii) Multiply the term number by 6 and subtract 4.
     (iv) Multiply the term number by 4 and subtract from 60.

2 Write down an expression for the nth term of each of the sequences in question **1**.

3 For the sequences with these nth terms find:
  (a) the first five terms in the sequence,
  (b) the tenth term of the sequence.
     (i) $9n$ **(ii)** $3n + 4$ **(iii)** $6n - 2$
     (iv) $18 - 2n$ **(v)** $40 - 5n$

4 Here are the first five terms of some sequences. Find an expression for the nth term of each of the sequences.
  (a) 6, 12, 18, 24, 30, ...   (b) 4, 7, 10, 13, 16, ...
  (c) 8, 9, 10, 11, 12, ...   (d) 28, 25, 22, 19, 16, ...
  (e) 5, 12, 19, 26, 33, ...   (f) 7, 6, 5, 4, 3, ...
  (g) 13, 8, 3, −2, −7, ...   (h) −7, −1, 5, 11, 17, ...

5 Find an expression for the nth term of each of these sequences:
  (a) odd numbers starting with 3
  (b) even numbers starting with 4
  (c) multiples of 11 starting with 11
  (d) even numbers starting with 8
  (e) odd numbers starting with 9
  (f) multiples of 4 starting with 16.

Exercise 6C   **Links 6C**

1 Here are the first four shapes in three sequences of shapes
    made from matchsticks:

(i)

Shape   Shape   Shape
number 1   number 2   number 3

Shape
number 4

(ii)

             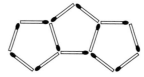

Shape   Shape   Shape
number 1   number 2   number 3

Shape
number 4

(iii)

Shape   Shape   Shape
number 1   number 2   number 3

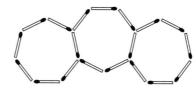

Shape
number 4

For each sequence:
(a) Work out the number of matchsticks in shape number 5 and shape number 6.
(b) Find an expression for the number of matchsticks in shape number n.
(c) Find the number of matchsticks in shape number 25.
(d) Find the number of the shape with 121 matchsticks.

2 Explain why each of the expressions in question 1 has '+1' as a term

3 Here are the first four shapes in a sequence of shapes made from matchsticks:

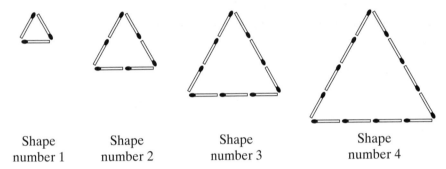

Shape	Shape	Shape	Shape
number 1	number 2	number 3	number 4

(a) Work out the number of matchsticks in shape number 5 and shape number 6.
(b) Find an expression for the number of matchsticks in shape number n.
(c) Find the number of matchsticks in shape number 42.
(d) Find the shape number of the shape with 81 matchsticks.

4 Here are four patterns of dots:

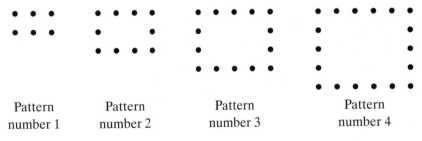

Pattern	Pattern	Pattern	Pattern
number 1	number 2	number 3	number 4

(a) Work out the number of dots in pattern number 5 and pattern number 6.
(b) Find an expression for the number of dots in pattern number n.
(c) Find the number of dots in pattern number 41.
(d) Find the pattern number of the pattern with 82 dots.

5   Here are four patterns made with square tiles:

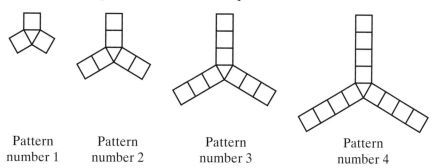

| Pattern
number 1 | Pattern
number 2 | Pattern
number 3 | Pattern
number 4 |

   (a) Work out the number of tiles in pattern number 5 and
       pattern number 6.
   (b) Find an expression for the number of tiles in pattern number n.
   (c) Find the pattern number with 99 tiles.
   (d) Find the number of tiles in pattern number 45.
   (e) Find the pattern number of the largest pattern that can be
       made with 200 tiles.

6   Here are four patterns made with kite shaped tiles:

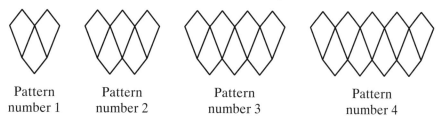

| Pattern
number 1 | Pattern
number 2 | Pattern
number 3 | Pattern
number 4 |

   (a) Work out the number of tiles in pattern number 5 and
       pattern number 6.
   (b) Find an expression for the number of tiles in pattern number n.
   (c) Find the number of tiles in pattern number 30.
   (d) Find the pattern number with 67 tiles.
   (e) Find the pattern number of the largest pattern that can be
       made with 50 tiles.

7   Here are four patterns made with black and white square tiles:

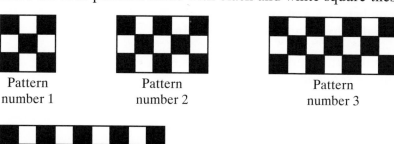

Pattern
number 1

Pattern
number 2

Pattern
number 3

Pattern
number 4

(a) Work out the number of white tiles and the number of black tiles in pattern number 5 and pattern number 6.

(b) Find an expression for the number of white tiles in pattern number n.

(c) Find an expression for the number of black tiles in pattern number n.

(d) Find the number of white tiles and the number of black tiles in pattern number 22.

(e) Find the pattern number of the shape with 49 white tiles.

(f) Find the pattern number of the shape with 38 black tiles.

(g) Find the highest pattern number that can be made with 100 black tiles.

Exercise 6D Mixed questions   Links 6D

1 Find the next three terms in each of these sequences:
   (a) first term = 7; rule is **add 4**
   (b) first term = 2; rule is **multiply by 3**
   (c) first term = 8; rule is **multiply by 5 and subtract 1**
   (d) first term = 13; rule is **subtract 6 then multiply by 4.**

2 For each of these sequences:
   (i) find the term to term rule for the sequence,
   (ii) find the next two terms in the sequence.

   (a) 2, 10, 50, 250, 1250, ...
   (b) 27, 9, 3, 1, $\frac{1}{3}$, ...
   (c) 22, 17, 12, 7, 2, ...
   (d) 1, 4, 10, 19, 31, ...

3 For each of these position to term rules, find:
   (i) the first five terms in the sequence,
   (ii) the eighth term in the sequence,
   (iii) an expression for the nth term of the sequence.

   (a) **Multiply the term number by 4 and add 6.**
   (b) **Multiply the term number by 5 and subtract 2.**
   (c) **Multiply the term number by 3 and subtract from 16.**

4 For sequences with these nth terms find:
   (i) the first five terms in the sequence,
   (ii) the fifteenth term of the sequence.
   (a) $6n$ (b) $2n + 11$ (c) $7n - 6$
   (d) $32 - 5n$ (e) $4 - 8n$

5 Here are the first five terms of some sequences.
   Find an expression for the nth term of each of the sequences.
   (a) 9, 16, 23, 30, 37, ...   (b) 11, 7, 3, −1, −5, ...
   (c) 0, 5, 10, 15, 20, ...   (d) 10, 4, −2, −8, −14, ...

6 The *n*th term of a sequence is $10n + 7$. A term of the sequence is 87. Find the term number of 87.

7 The *n*th term of a sequence is $14 - 3n$. A term of the sequence is -58. Find the term number of -58.

8 115 is a term of the sequence 3, 10, 17, 24, 31, …
Find the term number of 115.

9 -130 is a term of the sequence 14, 5, -4, -13, -22, …
Find the term number of -130.

10 Here are the first four shapes in a sequence of shapes made from matchsticks:

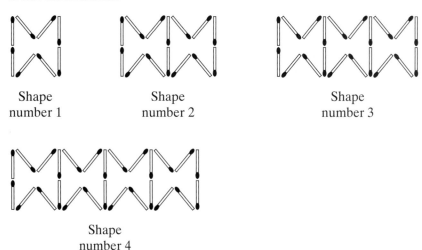

Shape
number 1

Shape
number 2

Shape
number 3

Shape
number 4

(a) Work out the number of matchsticks in shape number 5 and shape number 6.
(b) Find and expression for the number of matchsticks in shape number *n*.
(c) Find the number of matchsticks in shape number 17.
(d) Find the shape number of the shape with 170 matchsticks.
(e) Find the shape number of the largest shape that can be made with 200 matchsticks.

11 Here are four patterns made with black and white tiles:

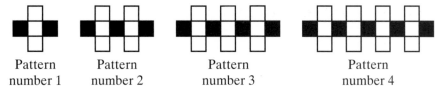

Pattern
number 1

Pattern
number 2

Pattern
number 3

Pattern
number 4

(a) Work out the total number of tiles in pattern number 5 and pattern number 6.
(b) Find an expression for the number of white tiles in pattern number *n*.
(c) Find an expression for the total number of tiles in pattern number *n*.

(d) Find the number of white tiles in pattern number 15.

(e) Find the total number of tiles in pattern number 20.

(f) Find the number of white tiles in the pattern with 8 black tiles.

(g) Find the total number of tiles in a pattern with 27 white tiles.

7 Properties of shapes

1 Construct a regular octagon inside a circle so that the vertices
are all on the circumference.
   (a) Draw two lines to divide the octagon into two trapezia
   and a kite.
   (b) Draw one line to create two pentagons.
   (c) Draw one line to create a quadrilateral. Name the two
   shapes that you now have.

2 The diagram shows part of a regular polygon:

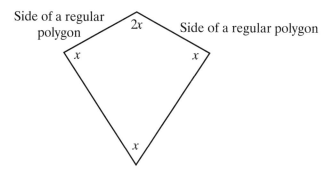

   Work out the number of sides the polygon has.

3 The diagram shows one sector of a regular polygon:

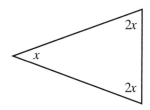

   Work out the number of sides the polygon has.

4 Construct a regular hexagon with vertices on the
circumference of a circle.
Draw two diagonals to create a kite.
   (a) Give the full mathematical name of the shapes that remain.
   (b) Find all the quadrilaterals that can be made by placing
   these two shapes together.

5 In each part, name those quadrilaterals which **must** have the
properties stated:
   (a) All sides are of equal length

      square   rectangle   parallelogram   rhombus   trapezium   kite

    (b) Only one pair of parallel sides

        square   rectangle   parallelogram   rhombus   trapezium   kite

    (c) Two pairs of parallel sides and no angle of 90°

        square   rectangle   parallelogram   rhombus   trapezium   kite

6 Construct a regular pentagon inside a circle so that the vertices are all on the circumference.
Label it *ABCDE*.
  (a) Complete and shade a sector.
  (b) Shade a segment.
  (c)   **(i)** Mark a chord.
        (ii) Mark an arc.

7 Construct a regular decagon inside a circle so that the vertices are all on the circumference.
Label it *ABCDEFGHIJ*.
Join *CE, BF, JF*.
Give the mathematical names of the four regions you have created.

8 *XY* is perpendicular to *OQ*.
PQR is a tangent to the circle, centre *O*.

Explain why $XQ = YQ$ and $PQ = QR$.

If angle $QRY = 30°$, show that *XQYO* is a rhombus.

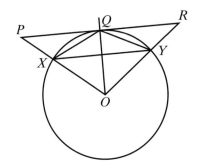

9 The circles are concentric with centre *O*.
Explain why $AB = BC$.

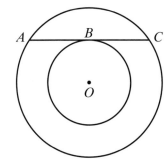

10

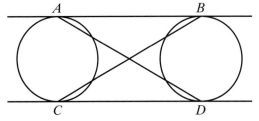

The circles are of equal size with *AB* and *CD* as common tangents.
AB is parallel to *CD*.
Explain why $AD = BC$.

11

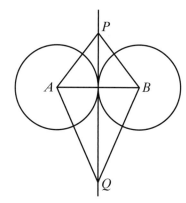

Two equal circles have a common tangent, *PQ*.
A and *B* are the centres of the circles.
Give reasons why *APBQ* must be a kite.

12 Show how three equal rhombuses can be drawn in a regular hexagon.

13 Give the full mathematical name for each of the shapes in the diagram.

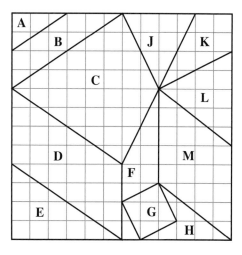

8 Symmetry and transformations

1   Copy each shape and draw in all lines of symmetry:

(a)   (b)    (c)   (d)

(e)   (f)

2   Copy each shape and indicate all planes of symmetry:

(a)   (b) 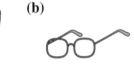   (c) 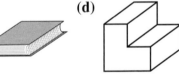   (d)

3   Write down the number of lines of symmetry for each shape:

(a)   (b)   (c)   (d)

4   Write down the order of rotational symmetry for the diagrams:

(a)   (b)   (c)   (d)

5 Copy and complete the diagram so that it has both diagonals as lines of symmetry:

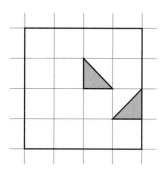

Write down the order of rotational symmetry.

6 Shade in ten squares to give the shape rotational symmetry order 4.

Draw a separate diagram with further squares shaded to give the tile line symmetry, order 4.

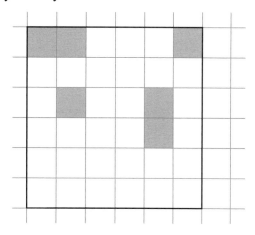

Exercise 8B   Links 8C

1 Draw the triangle $A\,(2, 3)$, $B\,(3, 5)$, $C\,(1, 4)$ and its reflection in the line $x = y$.

2 Draw the triangle $D\,(2, 1)$, $E\,(7, 1)$, $F\,(6, 3)$ and its reflection in the line $x = y$.

3 Draw the triangle $G\,(3, 2)$, $H\,(2, 5)$, $I\,(5, 5)$ and its reflection in the line $x = y$.

4 Draw the triangle $P\,(-4, 2)$, $Q\,(-1, 2)$, $R\,(-1, 6)$ and its reflection in the line $x = -y$.
Write down the coordinates of two invariant points on the shape.
(Invariant points are points that are still in the same position after the transformation.)

5 Draw the shape $S\,(-1, -2)$, $T\,(2, 2)$, $U\,(2, 5)$, $V\,(-1, 0)$.
Reflect this shape in the line $x = y$.
Write down the mathematical name for the region where shape and image overlap.

6 Triangle A (0, −1), B (3, −1), C (0, 3) is reflected in the line $x = 0$.
The original triangle and its image are reflected in the line $y = 0$.
The combined shape has 4 of its vertices on the coordinate axes.
Name the shape made by the lines joining these points.

7 Copy the following onto isometric paper and draw the reflection using the line shown as the mirror line.

(a)   **(b)**

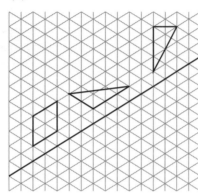 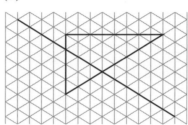

Exercise 8C   Links 8E

1 Translate the shape:

    (a) 3 units right and 1 unit up using column vector $\begin{pmatrix} 3 \\ 1 \end{pmatrix}$.

    (b) 6 units right and 2 units down using column vector $\begin{pmatrix} 6 \\ -2 \end{pmatrix}$.

    (c) 4 units left and 3 units up using column vector $\begin{pmatrix} -4 \\ 3 \end{pmatrix}$.

    (d) 3 units left and 4 units down using column vector $\begin{pmatrix} -3 \\ -4 \end{pmatrix}$.

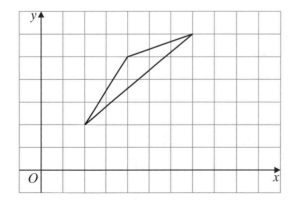

2 Translate the shape:

(a) $\begin{pmatrix} -3 \\ 5 \end{pmatrix}$ (b) $\begin{pmatrix} 4 \\ -2 \end{pmatrix}$ (c) $\begin{pmatrix} -2 \\ -3 \end{pmatrix}$ (d) $\begin{pmatrix} 0 \\ 5 \end{pmatrix}$

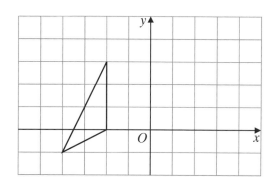

3 Translate the shape:

(a) $\begin{pmatrix} 4 \\ 1 \end{pmatrix}$ (b) $\begin{pmatrix} 8 \\ 3 \end{pmatrix}$ (c) $\begin{pmatrix} -1 \\ 2 \end{pmatrix}$ (d) $\begin{pmatrix} 1 \\ 3 \end{pmatrix}$

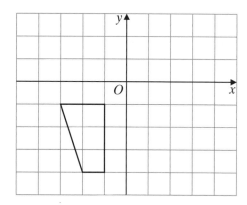

4 Describe fully the transformations which map:
   (a) **C** onto **A**   (b) **A** onto **B**
   (c) **C** onto **E**   (d) **D** onto **C**
   (e) **B** onto **E**   (f) **D** onto **B**.

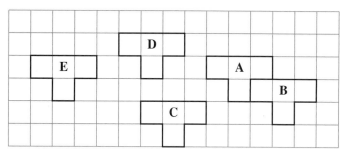

1 Rotate the shape in the diagram 90° clockwise, using each of the centres *P*, *Q*, *R* and *S* in turn:

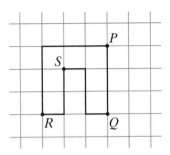

2 Draw the triangle *A* (1, 1), *B* (1, 3), *C* (2, 1).
Rotate the triangle by a quarter turn anticlockwise using
  (a) (3, 0) as centre
  (b) (−1, 0) as centre
  (c) (2, −2) as centre.

3 Draw the triangle *P* (1, 3), *Q* (3, 5), *R* (5, 3).
Rotate the triangle by a half turn using each of the centres
(1, 1), (3, 1) and (5, 1).

4 Rotate this shape 180° clockwise
  (a) using (3, 3) as centre
  (b) using (2, 1) as centre
  (c) using (−1, −1) as centre.

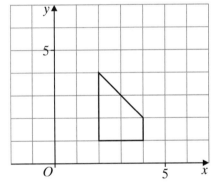

5 Copy the shapes onto isometric paper.
Using the centre marked,
  (a) rotate shape **A** clockwise by 60°, 120°, 180°, 240° and 300°.
  (b) rotate shape **B** clockwise by 120° and 240°.

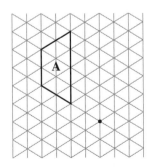

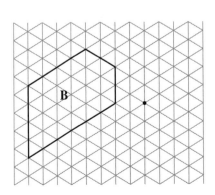

6 Describe fully each of the transformations:
    (a) **A** onto **C**   **(b)** **A** onto **B**
    (c) **E** onto **B**   **(d)** **A** onto **E**
    (e) **C** onto **B**   **(f)** **D** onto **A**.

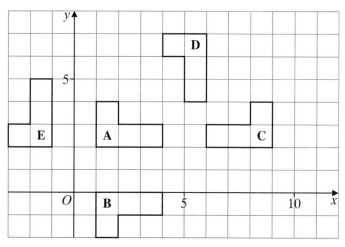

7 Describe fully each of the transformations:
    (a) **A** onto **B**   **(b)** **B** onto **C**
    (c) **A** onto **E**   **(d)** **D** onto **F**
    (e) **E** onto **F**   **(f)** **E** onto **D**
    (g) **C** onto **D**   **(h)** **A** onto **F**.

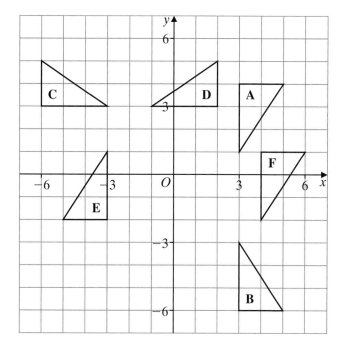

9 Angles, constructions and bearings

1   Measure these lines. Give your answers in both millimetres and centimetres.

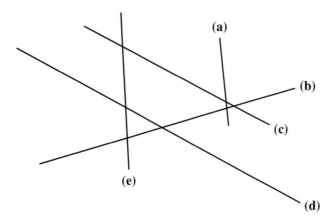

2   Draw, to the nearest mm, lines of length:
   (a) 34 mm   **(b)** 68 mm   **(c)** 2.7 cm
   (d) 4.2 cm   **(e)** 5.8 cm

3   Construct triangle *XYZ* with:
   (a) angle $X = 25°$, angle $Y = 70°$, $XY = 6$ cm.
   (b) angle $Y = 58°$, angle $Z = 43°$, $YZ = 5.4$ cm.
   (c) angle $X = 34°$, angle $Z = 109°$, $XZ = 4$ cm.
   (d) angle $Y = 123°$, angle $Z = 27°$, $YZ = 48$ mm.

4   Construct accurate figures for the diagrams shown:
   (a)

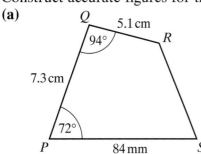

   Measure the length *RS*
   and angles *R* and *S*.

   (b)

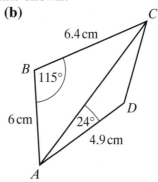

   Measure the length *DC*
   and angle *D*.

1 Construct an accurate net for this cuboid:

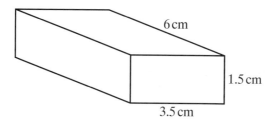

2 Sketch a net for this triangular prism:

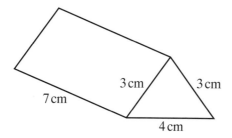

3 Draw an accurate net to construct a square-based pyramid:

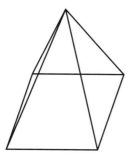

4 Draw a sketch of the shape that can be made from this net:

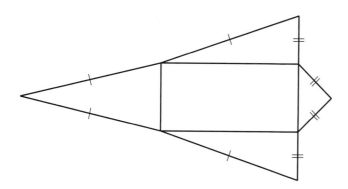

5 Could this be a net of a solid shape? Give a reason for your answer.

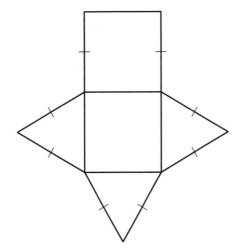

6 Which of these nets would make a cube?

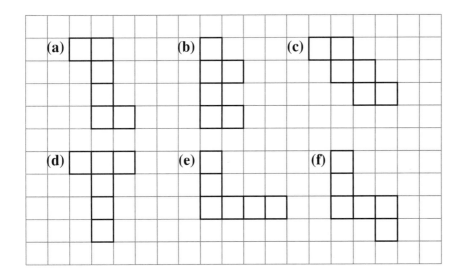

(a)

(b)

(c)

(d)

(e)

(f)

Exercise 9C   **Links 9C**

---

1 Find the marked angles:

(a)

(b)

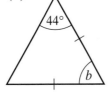

(c)

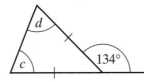

(d)

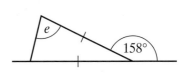

2 Work out the value of the letter:

(a)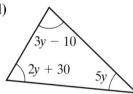

(b)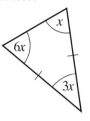

(c)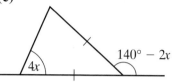

(d)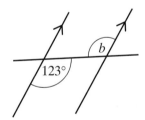

(e)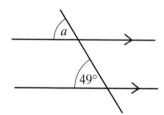

3 Give the size of *a*.
Give a reason for your answer.

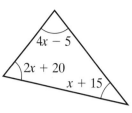

4 Give the size of *b*.
Give a reason for your answer.

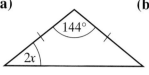

In each of the following questions, work out the size of the marked angles. You must give a reason or reasons for your answers.

5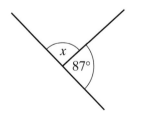

6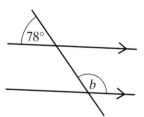

7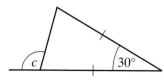

8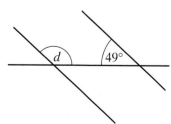

9

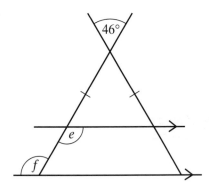

10

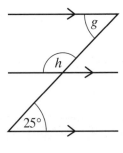

Exercise 9D   Links 9D

1 A regular pentagon has five sides.
   Work out the size of:
   (a) an exterior angle
   (b) an interior angle.

2 A regular polygon has interior angles of 160°.
   How many sides has it got?

3 Give the size of x:

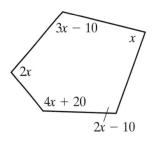

4 Work out the size of the missing angles in these quadrilaterals:
   (a)   **(b)**   **(c)**

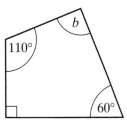   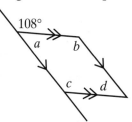   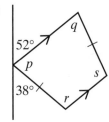

5 Use this diagram to show that the exterior angle of this
   triangle is 130°:

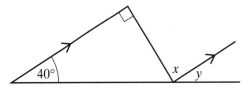

6 Explain why regular hexagons will tessellate, but regular pentagons will not.

7 Investigate the statement 'All triangles will tessellate'.

Exercise 9E Mixed questions   Links 9E

1 Construct an accurate drawing of the diagrams shown below:

(a)

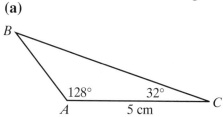

Measure the length *BC* to the nearest mm.

(b)

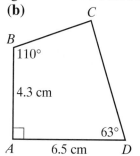

Measure the lengths *BC* and *CD* to the nearest mm.

2 Construct an accurate net for the regular tetrahedron shown below:

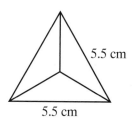

3 Which of these nets will construct a cuboid?

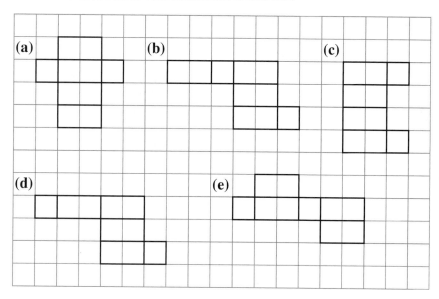

4   In each of these diagrams work out the size of the marked
angles. You must also give reasons for your answers.

(a)

y x $130°$

(b)

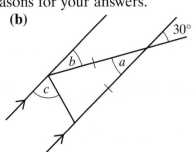
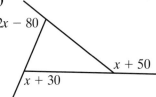

$30°$
b a
c

(c)

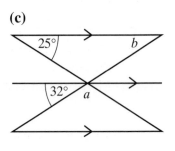

$25°$ b
$32°$ a

5   The sum of the interior angles of a regular polygon is $1800°$.
  (a) How many sides does the polygon have?
  (b) Calculate the size of the exterior angle of the polygon.

6   Work out the value of x, and hence the size of the marked
angles in each of the diagrams. Give reasons for your answers.

(a)

$200°$
$70°$ $60°$
$3x$ $70°$
x

(b)

$5x$
$3x$
$2x$

(c)

$2x - 80$
$x + 50$
$x + 30$

Exercise 9F   **Links 9F**

---

1   Using the map, find the
bearing of:
  (a) Cromer from Stevenage
  (b) Knebworth from Stevenage
  (c) Hitchin from Shefford
  (d) Cromer from Letchworth
  (e) Stevenage from Cromer
  (f) Hitchin from Letchworth
  (g) Hitchin from Stevenage
  (h) Hexton from Hitchin.

Shefford

Letchworth

Hexton

Hitchin   Cromer

Stevenage

Knebworth

2 *A*, *B* and *C* are three ships.
   B is due north of *A*.
   The bearing of *C* from *A* is 040°.
   The bearing of *B* from *C* is 260°.
   (a) Draw an accurate diagram showing the position of the
       three ships.
   (b) Measure the bearing of *C* from *B*.

3 The bearing of Leeds from Manchester is 052°.
   Work out the bearing of Manchester from Leeds.

4 The bearing of Plymouth from Exeter is 253°.
   Work out the bearing of Exeter from Plymouth.

5 Measure and write down the bearing of:
   (a) the radio mast from the lighthouse
   (b) the ship from the lighthouse
   (c) the ship from the radio mast
   (d) the lighthouse from the ship
   (e) the radio mast from the ship.

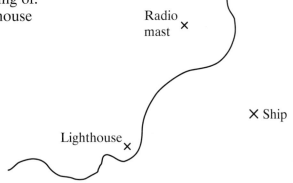

10 Handling data

1 Florence is conducting a survey into radio listening habits.
   She wrote the question:
                 'How much radio do you listen to?'
   Her friend Annie says this is not a good question. Write down
   two ways in which Florence could improve her question.

2 Jumana and Carl want to collect information about people's
   leisure activities.
   Design a suitable data capture sheet they could use.

3 Thirty bags of dark brown sugar are weighed.
   Here are the weights in grams, correct to the nearest gram:
   497 509 499 510 508 512 501 503 493 499
   501 507 497 495 498 511 496 507 502 504
   500 496 503 501 504 506 498 508 498 509
   Design and complete a tally chart and frequency table for this
   data. Use class intervals of 5 g.

4 Copy and complete this two-way table that provides
   information about the numbers of different types of sandwich
   sold at the canteen.

	White	Brown	Wholemeal	Total
Prawn		20		59
Cheese and pickle	40	23	13	
Egg	15	22		
Total	67		68	200

5 Design a data capture sheet to collect information about the
   types of shop in a town centre.

6 A class of 35 students were asked to provide information on
   how they travelled to school that day. The two-way table shows
   some of this information. Copy and complete the table.

	Walk	Bus	Car	Bicycle	Totals
Boys	6	3		1	
Girls			8	0	19
Totals	11				35

11 Probability

1 The probability of Rebecca winning a raffle prize is $\frac{5}{1200}$.
   Work out the probability of Rebecca *not* winning a raffle prize.

2 The probability of a new vacuum cleaner being faulty is 0.0003.
   Work out the probability of a new vacuum cleaner *not* being
   faulty.

3 A box of chocolates contains 4 toffees, 5 coffee creams, 7 nut
   clusters and 3 strawberry cups.
   A chocolate is to be chosen at random.
   Work out the probability of the chosen chocolate being:
   (a) nut cluster
   (b) toffee
   (c) either a toffee or strawberry cup
   (d) not a coffee cream.

4 The diagram shows a biased eight-sided spinner.
   Each section is labelled with one of the letters A, B, C, D, E,
   F, G, H.
   The probability of it landing on each section is shown in the
   table:

Section	A	B	C	D	E	F	G	H
Probability	0.08	0.13	0.05	0.11	0.09		0.14	0.07

   (a) Copy and complete the table.
   (b) Work out the probability the spinner will land on A or B.
   (c) Work out the probability it will not land on A or B.

5 A bus can be late, on time or early.
   The probability of it being late is 0.43.
   The probability of it being on time is 0.28.
   Work out the probability of it being early.

6 A fair dice is rolled.
   Work out the probability of the dice landing on:
   (a) a six
   (b) an even number
   (c) a prime number
   (d) a seven.

Exercise 11B   Links 11B

1 Stephen can lose, win or draw a game on his Playstation.
He plays two games.
List all the possible joint outcomes of his two games.

2 A game is played with a coin and a dice.
The coin is tossed once and the dice rolled once.
  (a) List all the possible joint outcomes when the coin is tossed
   and the dice rolled.
  (b) Use your list to work out the probability of getting a head
   and a six.

3 Leonie wants to buy a hot drink and a cake.
She has three choices of hot drink: tea, coffee or chocolate.
She has four choices of cake: ginger, banana, carrot or sultana.
List all the possible joint outcomes of the different choices she
could make.

4 Hussain spins this spinner twice.
He records the sum of the two
possible numbers upon which the
spinner lands.
Copy and complete the table.

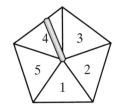

2nd spin

1st spin	1	2	3	4	5
1					
2					
3			7		
4					
5					

5 For Sunday dinner Patrick can choose:

chicken, lamb, beef or pork.

For pudding he can choose:

trifle, apple pie or rice pudding

  (a) List all the possible joint outcomes of choices Patrick
   could make.
  (b) If every choice is equally likely, work out the probability
   of Patrick choosing beef dinner and apple pie.

Examination style practice paper

Section 1   You must not use a calculator.

1 (a) Work out $(7 + 2) \times 5$.   (1)

   (b) Insert one pair of brackets in the expression
        $6 \times 5 - 3 + 1$ so that its value is 13.   (1)

2 (a) Find the value of $5x - 2y$ when $x = 4$ and $y = -3$.   (2)

   (b) Factorize $12n + 9$.   (1)

3 The table shows information about the mathematics GCSE
    entries at Mathstown High School:

	Foundation	Intermediate	Higher	Total
Boys		47		
Girls	12			103
Total	37	110		200

   (a) Complete the table.   (3)

   110 out of 200 entries were for the Intermediate tier.

   (b) Write 110 out of 200 as a percentage.   (2)

4 Work out $\dfrac{3}{5} \times \dfrac{7}{12}$.

   Give your answer as a fraction in its simplest form.   (2)

5

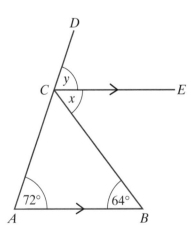

Diagram NOT
accurately drawn.

   ACD is a straight line.

   AB is parallel to CE.

   (a) (i)   Find the size of the angle marked x.

       (ii) Give a reason for your answer.   (2)

(b) Find the size of the angle marked y. (1)

6 Solve $4x^2 = 49$. (2)

7 Explain why it is possible to make a tessellation using
equilateral triangles and regular hexagons. (2)

Section 2   You may use a calculator.

1 (a) Find the cube of 4.23. (1)
(b) Find $\sqrt{8.41}$. (1)

2 $a = 5b - 3$.
Find the value of b when $a = 27$. (2)

3 In triangle ABC, $AB = 5.9\,\text{cm}$, $AC = 7.2\,\text{cm}$ and angle
$BAC = 67°$.
Make an accurate drawing of triangle ABC. (3)

4 A biased spinner has the numbers 1, 2, 3 and 4 on it.
The probability that the spinner will land on each of the
numbers 1 to 3 is given in the table:

Number	1	2	3	4
Probability	0.16	0.37	0.28	

Work out the probability that the spinner will land on the
number 4. (2)

5 Solve $6x - 1 = 2x + 5$. (3)

6 Write 600 as a product of its prime factors. (2)

7 Expand and simplify $3(2x - 1) - 2(x - 4)$. (2)

8 The size of each interior angle of a regular polygon is $156°$.
How many sides has the regular polygon got? (3)